If you could have any painting in the world, what would you choose?

Oh, decisions, decisions! I think it would be the *Duccio Madonna* that's in the National Gallery. It's so serene and tender and beautiful, and it's small enough to fit comfortably into my bedroom!

©Alamy

Who is your favourite singer or band?

He's no longer with us, alas, but I still have a very soft spot for Freddie Mercury of *Queen*.

Who's your favourite musician?

Ariana Grande, Taylor Swift and little mix

What would your ideal meal consist of?

I have very simple tastes — I'd like a big plate of vegetables with a cheese sauce, and then gooseberry fool.

My favourite meal would be:

You've met many famous people. Who made the biggest impression?

I think Graham Norton. I've been on his radio show several times, and he was kind and funny and a joy to chat to.

Which celeb would you like to meet?

What questions would you like to ask Jacky?

① ....
② ....
③ ....
④ ....
⑤ ....

Turn to page 94 to see Jacky interviewing Nick!

3

All About ME!

This JW Annual belongs to: Ava Chappel

I am 13 **years old**

MY FAVOURITES!

Colour
Pink

Animal

Tasty treat

Marvellous movie

Movie Script

JW book

JW character

My dream job is:

I'm happiest when:

So many new things to try!

HOW TO USE THIS BOOK!

- Work your way through all the games, makes, bakes and challenges — you can do them in any order you like!
- Tick off each thing when it's done.
- Fill in your congratulations certificates as you complete each section.
- Yay! Look at everything you've achieved!

BE A ROCKIN' WRITER!

Brush up your writing skills with my tips and challenges. You'll be creating bestsellers in no time!

This is to certify that Ava .... **has:**

- ☐ Read and practised Jacky's tips for writing
- ☐ Written a tale inspired by phone messages
- ☐ Created a lead character for their story
- ☐ Generated a story character cast
- ☐ Played the story spinner game
- ☐ Taken the book, blog or vlog test
- ☐ Swapped some new words for old

Congratulations!
You've reached Rockin' Writer Status

Jacky's Story

Tips from your favourite author!

Discover how I write!

Many of you ask me about how I write my stories and how to start a book. Not every idea turns into good book material, but I still have lots of fun trying them out.

AWESOME INSPIRATION!

A popular question is where do I get my inspiration from, and the answer is everywhere! It could be something you see or hear — you just never know when an idea might strike, so keep a notebook and pen handy. I always do.

Can you think of something that happened to you that might make a good story? Jot it down here:

Try writing some dramatic first sentences here:

JUMP RIGHT IN!

Often the best plan is to start your story with an attention-grabbing sentence that will suck the readers straight in. Look at the starting sentence of *Bad Girls*:

"They were going to get me."

Immediately you know something exciting is going to happen!

School!

THE CHARACTER GAME!

What will your character be like?

I can spend weeks thinking about the characters for a new book. It's as if I'm playing a very special imaginary game. I think it's the best part of writing a story.

Your main character doesn't even have to be a person, it could be an animal or even an alien! Who will star in your story?

Play with your character inside your head until they're as real as your best friend and then write a story about them!

Draw your character here:

Name: ....

Personality: ....

....

Likes: ....

....

Dislikes: ....

....

Turn to page 10 to create a character of your own!

Writer's Tool Kit!

What you need to become an Author Extraordinaire!

A pen is important to a writer. Carry one with you and you can scribble down ideas whenever you want!

Plan and write your story in a pretty notebook. Keep them to look back at your stories when you're older!

Type up your story. You can print it out and put it together like a book or share it online!

Develop your imagination and understand what makes a story exciting by reading lots of books!

Jacky's Top Tips!

Cut them out and pin them up for writing inspiration.

Get the Habit!
Try to write a little every day. Even if you just jot down a diary entry it helps you get used to turning your thoughts into words.

Have Fun!
Don't get too caught up in planning every story detail before you start writing. I like to surprise myself with what happens as the story develops!

Don't Worry!
If you get stuck with a story don't sit stressing about it. Get up and do something else and you might find the story starts to flow again. If it doesn't, leave it and move on to your next idea.

I often take Jackson for long walks to clear my head!

Imagine, Imagine, Imagine!
No idea is too crazy to make a great story. If you want to write about fairies or mythical creatures or space monsters, you can!

Nothing's Set in Stone!
You can go back and change the things you don't like. I make all sorts of false starts going over sentences again and again.

LITTER

Phone Fiction!

Use a text message as a story starter!

Pick your fave emoji to get your story starter text!

When you've tried our story starters, use your own texts!

WHY NOT?

Tell the whole story through a text message conversation!

Classroom Characters!

Your school supplies will help create a new hero for your story!

You'll need:
- ☑ Pencils
- ☑ Paper
- ☑ Calculator
- ☑ Highlighter

COLOURFUL PERSONALITY!

Use your highlighter to choose three personality traits for your character:

Naughty	Clumsy
Swotty	Lonely
Kind	Angry
Ambitious	Bossy
Chatty	Brave
Lazy	Stubborn
Nosy	Sporty
Spiteful	Messy

NUMBER NAME GAME!

Use your calculator and follow these instructions...

Write out the letters of the alphabet on a piece of paper, and give each letter a number — A=1, B=2, C=3 all the way through to Z=26. This is your code.

Now write out your own name and work out the number of each letter using your code. Use a calculator to add all the numbers together!

If your answer is 10 or more, add the digits together until you get a number between 1 and 9, for example 81 would be 8 + 1 = 9

Now choose the name that matches your number!

1. Iris Black
2. Lara Palmers
3. Lucy Star
4. Jemima Fleur
5. Stevie Cartwright
6. Melanie Moon
7. Ella Bunsen
8. Violet Truffle
9. Evangeline Childs

Use names of friends and family to create more characters!

SUBJECT MATCH!

Pick your favourite school subject from the schedule to choose an outstanding feature for your character!

MONDAY	TUESDAY	WEDNESDAY	THURSDAY	FRIDAY
English Can't read, but tries to keep it a secret		**Art** Only wears the colour black		**Science** LOVES animals of all kinds
	Maths Can calculate huge sums in their head		**Languages** Can't pronounce their Ws	**Geography** Has lived all over the world
Music Hums music all the time		**History** Always wears an antique ring	**PE** Walks with a limp	

Think About...
How does the feature affect your character? Do they feel special? Are they bullied because of it?

TAKE THE TEST!

Can you answer these questions about your character?

What's their favourite possession?

What do they eat for breakfast?

What after-school activity do they love?

What sort of clothes do they wear?

What upsets them most?

Now you've created a character, put all your elements together and write an exciting story!

Turn over for more!

FUNNY FAMILIES

Close your eyes and randomly point to the chart, the

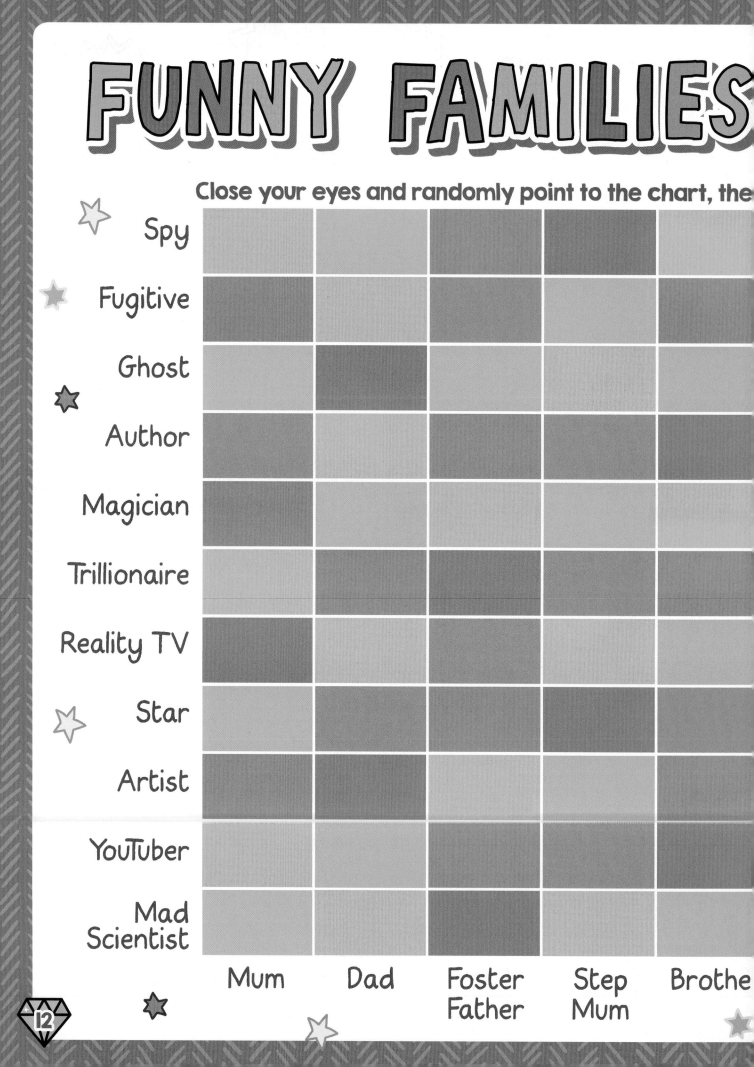

	Mum	Dad	Foster Father	Step Mum	Brothe
Spy					
Fugitive					
Ghost					
Author					
Magician					
Trillionaire					
Reality TV					
Star					
Artist					
YouTuber					
Mad Scientist					

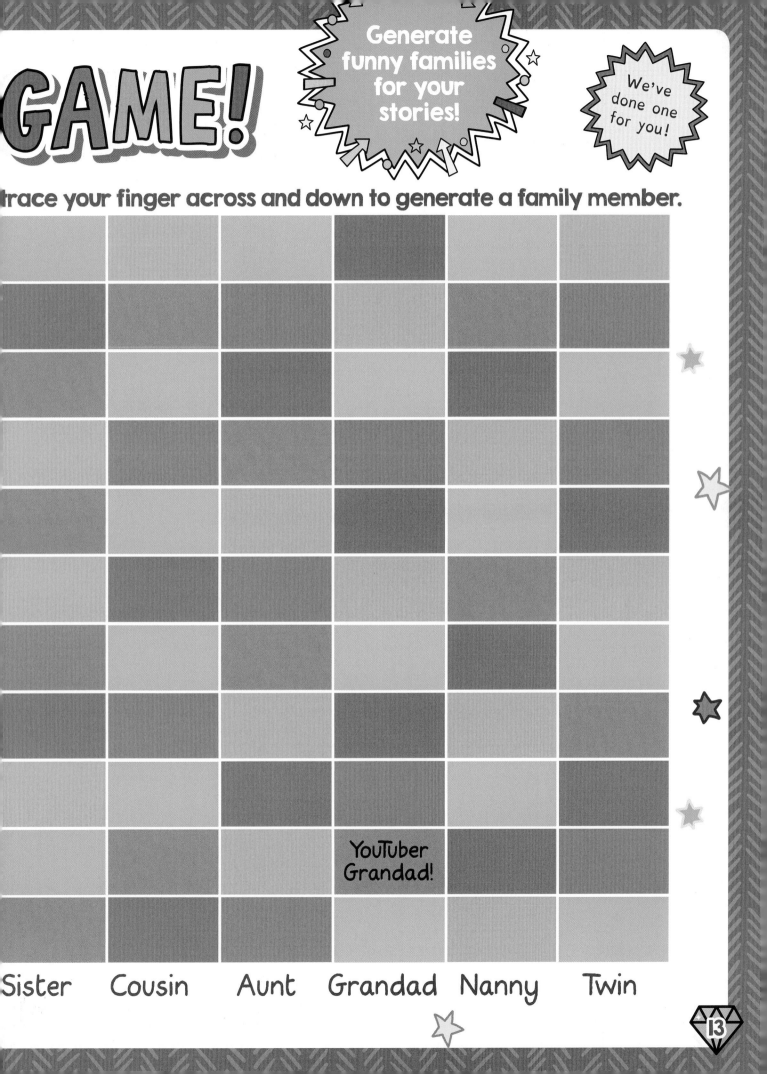

GAME!

Generate funny families for your stories!

We've done one for you!

Trace your finger across and down to generate a family member.

YouTuber Grandad!

Sister   Cousin   Aunt   Grandad   Nanny   Twin

13

Fidget Fiction!

Dig out your old fidget spinner and use it to write your next masterpiece!

Characters & Settings!

An absent-minded pirate

A kindly nurse

A mischievous girl

Clumsy fairy

OUTER SPACE

CASTLE RUINS

FUN HOUSE

ON A PLANE

FAIRGROUND

A ZOO

THE NORTH POLE

Posh celebrity

Funny fashion designer

14

FIND YOUR FUTURE

1 Which is the worst scenario?
b. Every book suddenly disappears
a. Imagination is made illegal
c. The internet was never invented

2 What might your teacher call you?
c. Chatterbox
a. Daydreamer
b. Sensible

3 What's your personality?
a. Quiet, thoughtful and imaginative
c. Bubbly, funny and friendly
b. Clever, organised and honest

4 Choose ONE thing to take to a desert island:
a. A notebook and pen
b. A new book
c. A camera

MOSTLY A

Amazing Author!

There's no doubt you were born to be an author. You can be found scribbling down your latest ideas, daydreaming about new characters and creating whole new worlds! Try writing something every day to practise and we're sure we'll see your books on the shelf right beside Jacky's one day!

TOP-TIP!
Got an amazing idea and don't have your notebook? Record it on your phone instead!

MOSTLY B

When it comes to books, you know your stuff and you're not afraid to say what you think. That's why you'd make a fab book blogger! The best thing is, you'd get to do ALL your fave things from reading and writing to photography and design! Write a review for a JW book to get started!

TOP-TIP!
Gain subscribers by uploading to your blog as often as you can and tagging your posts so people can find it!

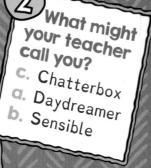

16

BOOK JOB!

5 Somebody gets out a camera, you...
- b. Smile politely
- a. Find somewhere to hide
- c. Yay! Selfie time!

6 What's the best thing about reading?
- c. Talking about it with friends
- a. Getting inspired
- b. Being transported to another world

7 What do you think makes a good book?
- a. Riveting writing
- c. Interesting characters
- b. A fabulous plot

Brilliant Blogger!

MOSTLY C

Vivacious Vlogger!

You could talk about books for hours. Seriously. Luckily, people can't get enough of listening to you! With all your energy and passion, people will flock to your channel to hear you gush about the latest book you read. Get out your phone and start experimenting with lighting, camera angles and editing!

TOP TIP!

Talking to a camera is weird at first and you might get a bit shy. Just imagine you're talking to your BFF to get over the awkwardness!

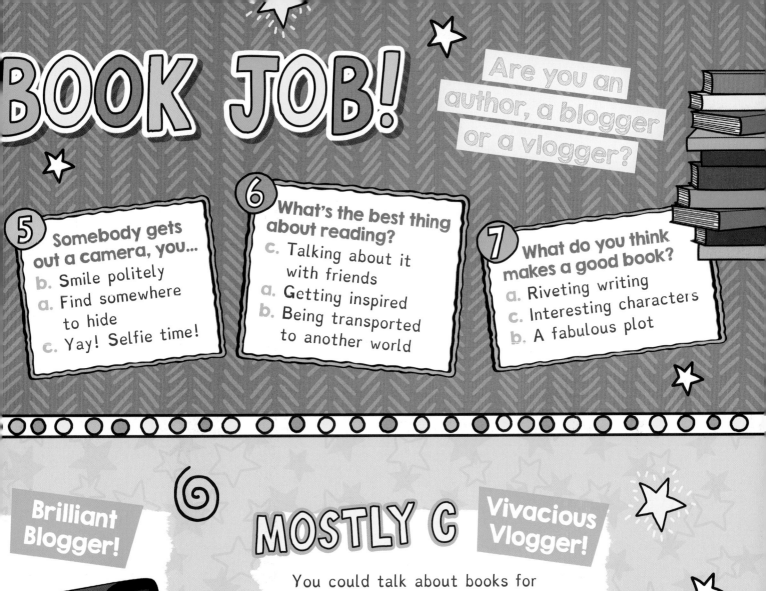

Turn over for more book, blog or vlog fun!

MOSTLY A — PEN NAME

Find your author pen name by finding the first letter of your first name and the last letter of your surname!

I'm Jacqueline Nesbit!

A - Agatha	N - Noel	A - Angelou	N - Nesbit
B - Beatrix	O - O'Brien	B - Brontë	O - Orwell
C - Charlotte	P - Pamela	C - Carrol	P - Potter
D - Dodie	Q - Queenie	D - Dahl	Q - Quentin
E - Enid	R - Robin	E - Edwards	R - Ransome
F - Frances	S - Sylvia	F - Fleming	S - Streatfeild
G - Gillian	T - Tove	G - Grimm	T - Tolkien
H - Harper	U - Ursula	H - Horowitz	U - Underhill
I - Isabel	V - Virginia	I - Ibbotson	V - Verne
J - Jacqueline	W - Winnie	J - Jansson	W - Wilson
K - Katherine	X - Xie	K - Kipling	X - Xin
L - Louisa May	Y - Yasmin	L - Lewis	Y - Young
M - Malorie	Z - Zora	M - Milne	Z - Zusak

MOSTLY B — BOOK REVIEW CARD

Use this template to help you write your book reviews!

	1	2	3	4	5
PLOT	☆	☆	☆	☆	☆
CHARACTERS	☆	☆	☆	☆	☆
SETTING	☆	☆	☆	☆	☆
THEME	☆	☆	☆	☆	☆

MOSTLY C — JW BOOK TAG!

Answer these questions and tag other BookTubers to get started!

1. What was the first JW book you read? _____

2. What's your fave JW book? _____

3. Which JW character are you most like, and why? _____
_____

4. If you could ask Jacky ONE question, what would it be? _____
_____

Always ask an adult for permission before uploading anything to a website, and always read the terms and conditions.

BE A WORD WIZARD!

Give your sentences a synonyms swap!

Words with similar meanings are called synonyms!

HAPPY
- Glad
- Joyful
- Cheerful
- Delighted
- Thrilled
- Elated
- Amused
- Ecstatic
- Merry
- Pleased

GOOD
- Stupendous
- Excellent
- Amazing
- Brilliant
- Fantastic
- Splendid
- Super
- Wonderful
- Marvellous
- Delightful

BIG
- Huge
- Giant
- Colossal
- Massive
- Tremendous
- Mammoth
- Ginormous
- Humongous
- Enormous
- Towering

WENT
- Danced
- Strolled
- Galloped
- Tiptoed
- Scurried
- Slithered
- Skipped
- Darted
- Hurried
- Glided

LAUGHED
- Roared
- Howled
- Giggled
- Chortled
- Cackled
- Shrieked
- Guffawed
- Snickered
- Whooped
- Sniggered

PRETTY
- Beautiful
- Stunning
- Gorgeous
- Striking
- Lovely
- Elegant
- Exquisite
- Handsome
- Fair
- Dazzling

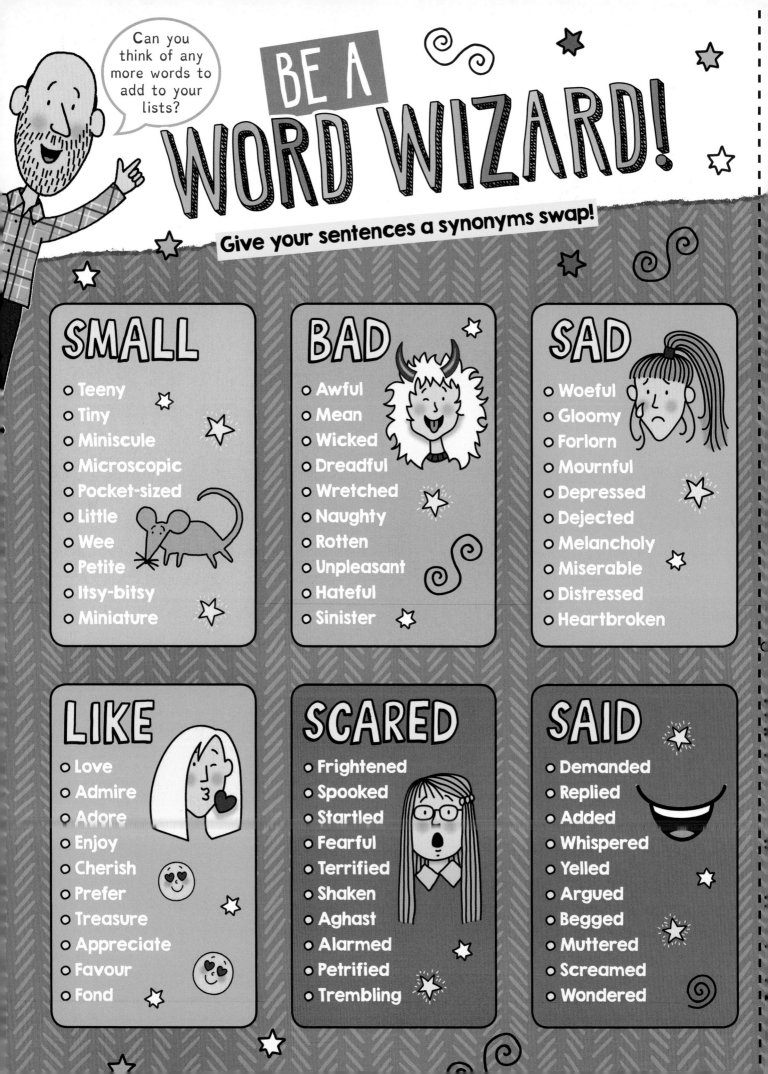

Can you think of any more words to add to your lists?

BE A WORD WIZARD!

Give your sentences a synonyms swap!

SMALL
- Teeny
- Tiny
- Miniscule
- Microscopic
- Pocket-sized
- Little
- Wee
- Petite
- Itsy-bitsy
- Miniature

BAD
- Awful
- Mean
- Wicked
- Dreadful
- Wretched
- Naughty
- Rotten
- Unpleasant
- Hateful
- Sinister

SAD
- Woeful
- Gloomy
- Forlorn
- Mournful
- Depressed
- Dejected
- Melancholy
- Miserable
- Distressed
- Heartbroken

LIKE
- Love
- Admire
- Adore
- Enjoy
- Cherish
- Prefer
- Treasure
- Appreciate
- Favour
- Fond

SCARED
- Frightened
- Spooked
- Startled
- Fearful
- Terrified
- Shaken
- Aghast
- Alarmed
- Petrified
- Trembling

SAID
- Demanded
- Replied
- Added
- Whispered
- Yelled
- Argued
- Begged
- Muttered
- Screamed
- Wondered

Become a STAR BAKER!

Our easy instructions will help you become a stellar chef!

This is to certify that

.... Ava .... has:

- [ ] Perfected Hetty's Victoria Sponge
- [ ] Made scones fit for a queen
- [ ] Baked their own bread
- [ ] Recreated Jacky's favourite cakes
- [ ] Filled a lunchbox with yummy snacks
- [ ] Created show stopping party snacks
- [ ] Made Nick Sharratt's ginger snap recipe

Congratulations!

You've reached Star Baker Status

Hetty's PERFECT VICTORIA SPONGE

DID YOU KNOW?
The cake is named after Queen Victoria who loved a slice of cake or two for an afternoon treat.

> Sssh! Don't tell Mrs B I found a quick way to make her signature bake!

This is a super-easy recipe — all the ingredients go in one bowl, so you don't have to spend forever beating different things together.

You'll need:

- ☑ 4 large eggs
- ☑ 225g softened butter cut into chunks
- ☑ 225g caster sugar
- ☑ 225g self-raising flour
- ☑ 2 level tsp baking powder

1 Pre-heat your oven to 180°C. Line and grease two 20cm sponge tins.

2 Break the eggs into a large mixing bowl. Now add the ingredients in this order:

- Sugar
- Sift in the flour and baking powder
- Butter

3 Beat with a mixer or by hand until all the ingredients are well combined. Don't overbeat or your cake won't rise - the mixture should easily drop off a spoon.

WHY NOT?
Add some fresh fruit to create a lovely celebration cake.

THE FILLING!

You'll need:
- ☑ 200g sifted icing sugar
- ☑ 100g soft butter
- ☑ 3 tablespoons of jam

1. Add the butter to the icing sugar and blend it together. You can use a wooden spoon, hand mixer or a fork. Beat the mix till it's soft and creamy.

2. Put the jam in a little bowl and give it a good stir. When it's smooth, spread on top of one of your sponge cakes. Now spread your buttercream on top.

3. Pop on the other half of your cake and dust the top with icing sugar or a sprinkle of caster sugar.

Enjoy!

FLOUR

DID YOU KNOW?
A traditional Victoria sandwich always has a buttercream icing and raspberry jam filling with a dusting of icing sugar on top.

4 Divide the mix evenly between your two tins and smooth flat on top. Bake for 25 minutes, checking them after 20.

5 Your cakes are ready when they're golden brown on top and slightly coming away from the edge of the tins. Gently press the top and, if it springs back, they're done!

6 Leave to cool in the tins for 10 minutes, then turn out on to a cooling rack. Leave to cool completely while you make your filling.

Super Fancy Scones

No fuss, no rolling, no cutting out and hardly any washing up!

You'll need:

- ☑ 200g self-raising flour
- ☑ 50g cold butter
- ☑ 125ml milk
- ☑ ½ tsp salt
- ☑ ½ tsp baking powder

Flavour Station

Spice up your scones with some tasty extra ingredients!

- ✿ 50g of sultanas or raisins
- ✿ 50g finely grated cheese
- ✿ ½ tsp of grated orange zest + 50g of candied peel
- ✿ 1 level tsp of mixed spice + 25g of brown sugar
- ✿ 25g freeze dried raspberries + 25g of caster sugar
- ✿ 50g chopped glace cherries
- ✿ 50g of chocolate chips
- ✿ 1 tsp of grated lemon zest + 25g of chopped candied ginger

Fancy Fillings:
Whipped cream
Jam
Orange marmalade
Sour cream and chive
Lemon curd
Peanut butter
Banana

What to do:

1 Pre-heat your oven to 220°C. Sift the flour, salt and baking powder into a large bowl. Cut the butter into chunks and add it to the bowl.

2 Use your fingertips to rub the butter into the flour. After about 10 minutes your mix should look like breadcrumbs.

3 If you're adding any extra ingredients like cheese or fruit, stir them through the crumb mix. Now add all the milk and use a butter knife to stir it all into a soft dough.

WHY-NOT?

Sprinkle the tops with brown sugar or drizzle sweet strawberry scones with some water icing.

from my kitchen ♥

TIP!

Shake the bowl and any big lumps will come to the top. Keep rubbing till all the chunks of butter have blended in.

FLOUR

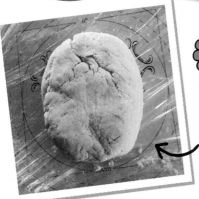

4 Cover your work surface with cling film and dust with some flour. Tip out the dough and lightly knead it until smooth.

5 Use your fingertips to flatten the dough into a rough rectangle around 1cm thick. Cut into squares then into triangles like these and place on a lined baking tray. Now roll all the mess into the cling film and throw it away – cleaning up done!

6 Brush the tops with a little milk and bake for 8 – 12 minutes until well risen and golden on top. Leave to cool then enjoy with your fave scone fillings.

25

Biscuit's BREAD BAKE!

Learn how to bake your own bread!

Makes one small loaf!

It really works!

Always ask an adult to help you in the kitchen!

You'll need:
- 225g plain or bread flour
- 1 fast action dried yeast sachet
- 100ml warm water
- 3 tbsp oil
- ½ tsp salt
- 1 zip lock plastic bag
- 1 loaf pan

1 Preheat your oven to 220°C or gas mark 7.

2 Add all the ingredients to the plastic bag, then carefully squeeze out any air and make sure it's fully sealed.

26

3 Squish the mixture through the bag to mix everything together. Do this until the dough starts to unstick from the sides. Leave for 10 minutes, then squish some more.

4 Sprinkle flour on your work surface, then take the dough out of the bag and knead it until it's smooth and doesn't stick.

15 – 20 minutes

5 Grease a loaf pan with oil, put the dough into it and mould it to the shape of the pan, then cover it with a towel for 20-30 minutes to let it rise.

6 Pop the loaf pan in the oven for 15 – 20 minutes until golden brown. Let it cool a little and tap on the bottom – if it sounds hollow it's ready!

Once you've mastered our basic bread recipe, try adding extra ingredients! You could use sundried tomatoes, herbs or seeds.

Coffee & Cookies

My mum worked at Roberts the cake shop. I thoroughly enjoyed all the extra bath buns and currant slices and apple puffs.

We've transformed Jacky's favourite coffee and walnut cake recipe into delish cupcakes with a hidden surprise!

You'll need:
- 12 cream-filled biscuits (we used Oreos)
- 2 eggs
- 110g soft butter or margarine
- 55g caster sugar
- 55g light brown sugar
- 110g self-raising flour
- 1 tsp baking powder
- 4 tsp instant coffee

1 Heat the oven to 180°C and place 12 cupcake cases in a bun tin. Pop a biscuit into the bottom of each case.

Ask an adult to dissolve the coffee in half a cup of boiling water and set aside to cool.

2 Put the eggs, sugar, flour, baking powder and butter into a bowl and beat together until you have a soft cake batter. Ask an adult to help with the mixer. Now stir in two tablespoons of your cooled coffee.

3 Carefully fill the cases with batter, hiding your cookie surprise! Bake for 15–18 minutes until golden and springy to touch. Leave to cool completely.

Cupcakes!

TO DECORATE

You'll need:
- 125g softened butter
- 225g icing sugar
- 1 tbsp of coffee mix
- Cocoa powder to dust
- Walnut halves

freshly baked ♥

1 Mix the sugar and butter together until you get a soft icing. Now mix in the coffee and stir to get a thick glaze.

2 Dip the cupcakes into the glaze to evenly cover the tops — don't put on too much or it'll drip down the sides!

3 Dust the tops with a sprinkle of cocoa and add a walnut half. Leave for 15 minutes to let the glaze set then they're ready to eat — yum!

Surprise inside!

Super Chocolate Change-Up!

Leave the coffee mix out of the cake batter and instead add 3 heaped tablespoons of cocoa powder and 2 tablespoons of milk.

To make the cookie crumble frosting, leave out the coffee mix and add 2 extra tablespoons of icing sugar and two or three crushed biscuits.

Add a mini Oreo topper too!

I'm tasty!

LUNCHBOX MUFFINS!

You'll need:
- ☑ 4 large eggs
- ☑ A selection of your favourite fillings
- ☑ Sprinkle of salt and pepper
- ☑ 2 tablespoons milk or water
- ☑ Grated cheese (optional)

Brighten up a boring lunchbox with these little treats!

what to do:

1 Pre-heat your oven to 200°C and grease the holes in a muffin or cupcake tin. Chop up your selected fillings, stir them together and pop them into the tin.

2 Crack the eggs into a bowl and lightly whisk together with the salt, pepper and milk or water.

Makes 6 muffins or 10 small ones made in a cupcake tin.

3 Carefully pour your egg mix over muffin fillings. Sprinkle some cheese on top of each one, then bake in the oven for 20 minutes.

4 When the muffins are puffy and golden brown, turn out of the tins on to a cooling rack. Enjoy warm for breakfast or leave to cool and pack into your lunchbox.

WHY NOT?
Spice up the muffins by mixing a pinch of chilli flakes or a dash of hot sauce into the egg mix.

FILLING STOP
Pick your favourites!

- [ ] Red and green peppers
- [ ] Carrots
- [ ] Spring onions
- [ ] Broccoli
- [ ] Mushrooms
- [ ] Tomatoes
- [ ] Shredded kale
- [ ] Ham
- [ ] Chicken
- [ ] Basil, parsley or coriander
- [ ] Bean sprouts
- [ ] Feta cheese — crumble instead of grating
- [ ] Olives
- [ ] Sun-dried tomatoes
- [ ] Spinach

Little Darlings

SOUND BITES!

These microphone cupcakes will steal the show at any party!

Always ask an adult for help in the kitchen!

You'll need:

- 350g sponge cake
- 150g buttercream icing
- Baking parchment
- Mini ice cream cones
- White candy melts
- Black food colouring
- Chocolate bean sweets
- Silver sprinkles

1 Blitz the cake in a blender to make crumbs. Spoon the icing into the cake crumbs and mix well. Roll the mix into large, equal-sized balls that fit into the cones.

Don't have a blender? Crumble the cake with your fingers instead!

2 Line a tray with baking parchment. Place the balls on the tray and pop in the freezer for at least 10-15 minutes.

3 Prepare the candy melts by following the instructions on the pack. Add a few drops of black colouring to turn the mixture grey.

4 Fill the cones with sweets. This will stop them from toppling over and add a yummy surprise inside! Spread a little of the candy melts around the inside rim of the cones. Place the cake pops on top and leave to set.

5 Carefully dip a cone pop into the grey melts. Gently tap off any excess, then cover in sprinkles or silver balls while it's still wet. Leave to harden before sharing with your BFFs!

WHY NOT?

Make some rockin' wraps to go around your cupcakes?

Desserts

UNICORN CANDY BARK!

Colourful and sparkly, just like a unicorn!

Treats to make your party rock!

They're show-stopping!

You'll need:

- White candy melts
- A selection of coloured candy melts
- A variety of sprinkles and decorations

Always ask an adult for help in the kitchen!

1 Line a baking tray with baking paper or tin foil.

2 Follow the pack instructions to melt the white and coloured candy melts in separate bowls.

3 Pour the white melted candy into the tray. Use the back of a spoon to smooth it out evenly.

4 Drizzle the other colours over the white candy and use a toothpick to make swirly patterns. Try to be quick as the candy will begin to set!

5 Finish with a flurry of sprinkles and your favourite decorations. We used edible glitter for extra sparkle!

6 Pop in the fridge to harden. Once set, break the bark into pieces and enjoy!

33

Nick's GINGER NUT NO-BAKE!

Try my favourite magic recipe!

Ingredients:

- ☑ 1 pack of ginger nut biscuits
- ☑ 300ml whipping cream
- ☑ Small packet of flaked almonds or a chocolate bar

Always ask an adult to help you in the kitchen!

INSTRUCTIONS:

1. Whip the cream until it's stiff enough to spread.

2. Spread lots of cream on to a biscuit and sandwich it to the next one, then stand them on a plate. Keep going until you've made a full ring!

3. When all the biscuits have been added, fill in the gaps with cream and smooth the surface of the ring with a butter knife.

4. Cover your creation with a large bowl and pop it in the fridge overnight. The biscuits will magically soften into a sponge and it will be firm enough to cut into slices in the morning!

5. Top off your cake with flaked almonds or grated chocolate!

DRAW AND DOODLE
Like a Pro!

I'll share my sketching tricks with you!

This is to certify that

.............ava............... has:

- ☐ Practised **Nick Sharratt's** colour tips
- ☐ Created awesome sketching effects
- ☐ Learned how to draw faces and hands
- ☐ Been inspired by famous artists
- ☐ Taken the **C**ircles and **S**quares Challenge
- ☐ Doodled funny animals
- ☐ Coloured a brilliant poster

Congratulations!
You've reached **Amazing Artist Status**

SKETCH BOOK

Nick's COLOUR CLASS!

Use a colour wheel to help you pick colours for your art!

Primary Colours!

You can make all the other colours by mixing together different amounts of RED, BLUE and YELLOW!

Mix Maths!

Mix two primary colours to get secondary colours:

⬤ + ⬤ = ⬤

⬤ + ⬤ = ⬤

⬤ + ⬤ = ⬤

Mix together primary and secondary colours to get the colours in between!

Colour wheel labels: Yellow, Yellow-Green, Green, Blue-Green, Blue, Blue-Violet, Violet, Red-Violet, Red, Red-Orange, Orange, Yellow-Orange

Inner labels: G, Y, O, B, R, V

Tints & Shades!

Any colour + ⬜ = Tint

Any colour + ⬛ = Shade

My favourite colour is:

36

Colour Effects!

For a gentle, calm effect, use colours that are next to each other on the wheel. Artists call these colours analogous.

Choose colours from opposite sides of the wheel for an energetic look! These are called complementary colours. Mix them together and see what you get!

Use primary colours to give a bold, cheerful pattern!

For a cold effect, pick the shades on the left side of the colour wheel — blues, purples or greens.

For a warm feel, use colours on the right of the wheel — reds, yellows and oranges.

For extra impact, add in some white or black to your patterns!

37

Draw Like NICK SHARRATT!

Make your drawings look amazing!

I'll tell you my secrets!

SKETCHING SECRETS!

Lots of Dots!
Draw dots to create a rough, stubbly effect. Try it when drawing facial hair or a garden wall. It's called stippling!

Cross-Hatching
This technique can be used to create dark patches and shadows. Just draw lots of lines one way, then lots of lines in the opposite direction over the top.

Blending
Press the pencil down hard and gradually become more gentle as you colour in. This will make the object you're colouring look less flat.

PAINTING PRO TIPS!

ACRYLICS AND POSTER PAINT
Using either of these will create a bright and bold picture. Use them when you want a colour to stand out when you're making signs or posters!

WATERCOLOURS
These paints will make your picture look dreamy or aged. Paper can easily rip using this technique — try a thicker card or special watercolour paper instead.

GET THRIFTY!
Who says you need a paintbrush? Experiment with sponges, an old toothbrush or even your fingerprints to see what effect you get!

LIGHT AND SHADE!

Make your drawings look real by adding light and shade. Notice where the light is coming from and the shadow it creates.

Take a look at this box — the light is hitting the top so the front is in shade. To sketch it, use a lighter blue where the light hits the surface and a darker blue to show where the light can't reach.

SPIN A SKETCH!

Use the torch on your phone as a light source!

Spin once to find an object to draw, spin again for the technique you'll use and one more time to pick the lighting!

Get thrifty

Lots of dots

Cross-hatching

Blending

Watercolours

Poster paints

39

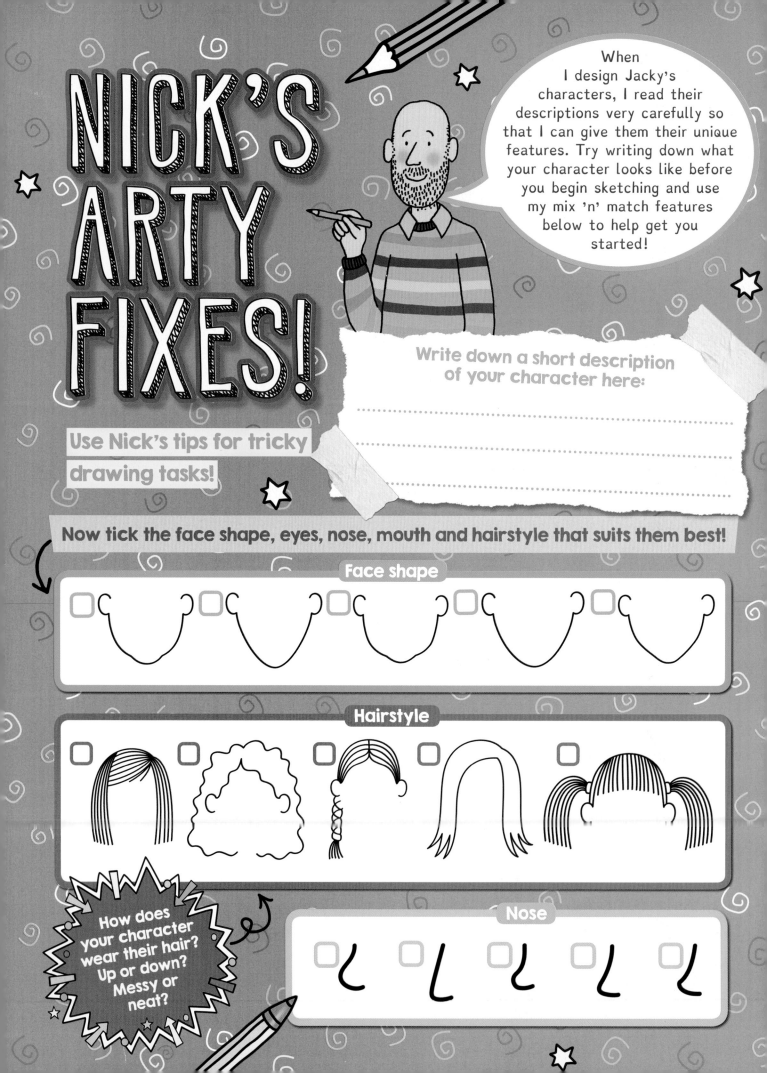

NICK'S ARTY FIXES!

When I design Jacky's characters, I read their descriptions very carefully so that I can give them their unique features. Try writing down what your character looks like before you begin sketching and use my mix 'n' match features below to help get you started!

Use Nick's tips for tricky drawing tasks!

Write down a short description of your character here:

....

....

....

Now tick the face shape, eyes, nose, mouth and hairstyle that suits them best!

Face shape

Hairstyle

How does your character wear their hair? Up or down? Messy or neat?

Nose

Drawing hands is sooo hard! How do you draw them?

My secret is to sketch five banana shapes! It's much easier than worrying over finger shapes and fingernails because it's obvious what they are! Try it for yourself using my speedy sketch tutorial.

① ② ③

Eyebrows show what your character is feeling – choose downwards sloping eyebrows for a worrier!

Eyes and eyebrows

Mouth

Assemble your character here!

Market Scene by L.S. Lowry

Create a crowd scene!

When I was a boy, the artist LS Lowry was incredibly popular. His scenes could often be filled with hundreds of people, going to work or to the fair or to football matches...

Lowry's work inspired me to have a go at creating my own crowd scenes. I did this market scene when I was nine!

Art Class!

I would start at a bottom corner and draw one figure and then another until I'd worked my way right across the paper. Give it a try yourself!

©The Lowry Collection, Salford

Nick's ART

The Seine at la Grande Jatte by Georges Seurat

This artist has created a delightful river scene from thousands of tiny dabs of paint. It's a way of working called pointillism and Seurat made the technique famous!

Art Class!

Here's a picture from *Midnight* where I've used dots to create different grey tones. You can make different shades depending on how closely or far apart you draw your dots!

Your next project — lots of dots!

42

Augustin Edouart

Augustin Edouart was a famous silhouette artist. Silhouettes are outline images filled with a solid colour, usually black, that have the same effect when you look at them as sharp shadows on a wall.

Let my favourite paintings and artists inspire YOU!

Art Class!

They were a popular art form in Victorian times and I thought they'd be a perfect way to illustrate Hetty Feather! Start with a basic shape and carefully add in some details.

Try this very Victorian art form!

CLUB!

The Railway by Édouard Manet

This is a terrific picture, painted by Édouard Manet, a French artist from a group known as the Impressionists. The girl has been painted from behind so we have to imagine what she looks like — it can be a useful way to give your pictures a certain atmosphere and a little bit of mystery!

Art Class!

This is one of my old student sketches. Choose a person from the picture and try sketching them from the front — it's up to you what they look like!

Sketch in reverse!

Circles & Squares!

Play this sketch game with your friends!

NICK'S AWW-SOME ART!

These doodle designs are so cute!

All you need is washable felt tips and paper!

BUTTERFLY

1. Colour your thumb and index finger. Press your thumb diagonally onto the page so they join at the bottom, then do the same underneath with your index finger.

2. Now draw a body, a face and two antennae where the wings meet!

WHY NOT? Give the wings a pretty pattern!

BUDGIE

1. Simply colour your index finger and press it vertically on the page.

2. Then draw a beak, a wing, a tail and two feet.

Use two different colours at once for a two-toned effect!

DOG

1. Colour your ring finger. Press it down horizontally, then press down again using only your fingertip to create a head.

2. Draw two legs, eyes and ears and a little nose.

This puppy looks like Jess Beaker's dog Alfie!

RABBIT

1. Colour your index finger, then press it down horizontally and again just above or below the first print.

2. Add long ears, a face and whiskers and – of course – a fluffy tail!

WHY NOT? Use your animal prints to decorate greetings cards!

CREATE YOUR OWN!

Use our chart below to get started. Simply find the month you were born and your favourite colour to discover what animal to make from your fingerprints!

	JAN-MARCH	APRIL - JUNE	JULY - SEPT	OCT - DEC
PINK	DOLPHIN	PENGUIN	CRAB	KOALA
YELLOW	HAMSTER	DEER	LEMUR	PIG
PURPLE	CAT	BAT	FROG	TIGER
BLUE	WHALE	OWL	TORTOISE	BEE
RED	DUCK	LADYBIRD	SHEEP	PONY
GREEN	FISH	HEDGEHOG	LION	SNAIL

FOX

1. Colour your index finger. Create a heart shape by pressing down diagonally one way, then the other so the bottom merges together.

2. Draw an outline with ears, add a nose and two smiley eyes.

WHY NOT?
Add a big bushy tail to the side using your thumb!

LLAMA

1. Colour your thumb and index finger. Press your thumb down horizontally, then press your index finger down diagonally on top.

2. Make the outline of the body and head look as fluffy as a cloud, add four legs, an eye, a mouth and long ears.

To create an alpaca, just make the ears short and round!

MOUSE

1. Colour your index finger and press it down vertically, then press down with just your fingertips for ears.

2. Draw two eyes, a nose and some whiskers!

Try creating a wedge of cheese as an extra challenge!

PEACOCK

1. Colour your index finger and press it down a few times to form a fan shape.

2. Draw a long neck, two eyes, a beak, two feet and some feathers on the top of its head.

Use lots of different colours for a pretty effect!

47

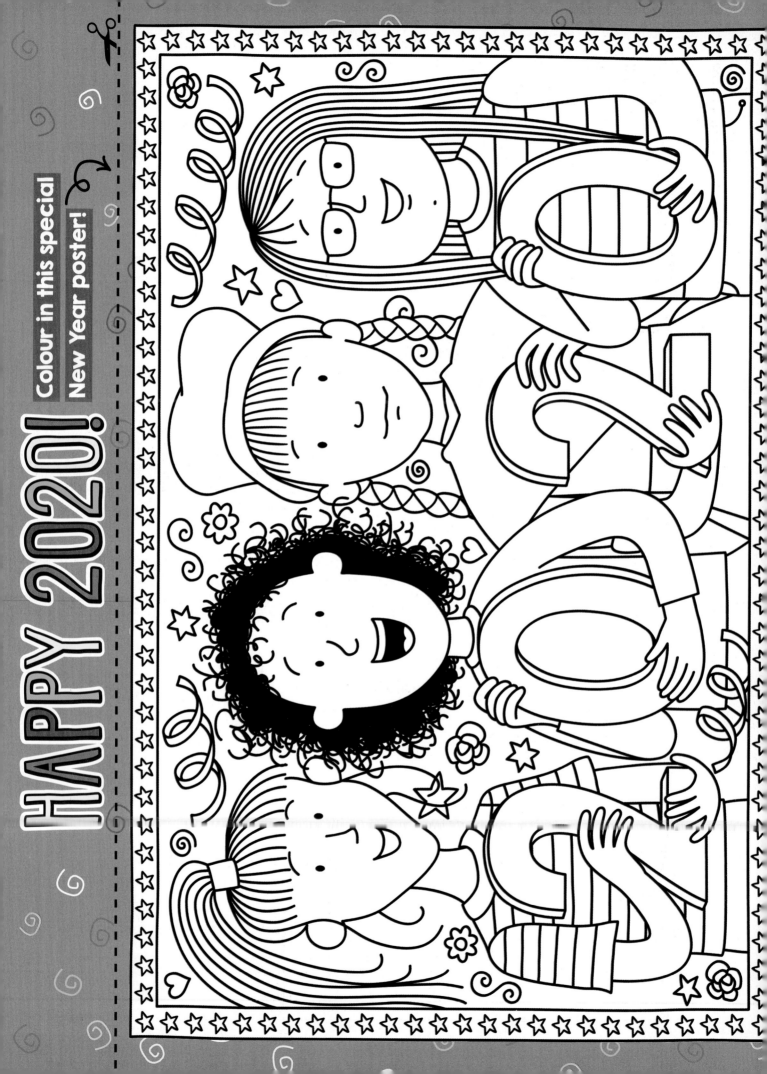

Become a CRAFT QUEEN

Make, sew and upcycle with us!

We'll help you create outstanding crafts!

This is to certify that

..........Ava.......... has:

- ☐ Learned to sew a cute kitten jumper
- ☐ Made a desktop stationery station
- ☐ Crafted a pop-tastic pillow
- ☐ Nailed the upcycle challenge
- ☐ Made their own modelling clay
- ☐ Made brilliant bookmarks
- ☐ Turned scraps into something amazing
- ☐ Transformed a sock into a donut!

Congratulations!
You've reached Craft Queen Status

49

Turn an old school sweater into a gorgeous Jacob jumper!

You'll need: ➤
- ☑ Grey jumper or sweatshirt
- ☑ Chalk
- ☑ Black and pink embroidery thread
- ☑ Needle

1 Use the chalk to copy this Jacob face on to your jumper.

2 Sew along the lines with black thread – use back stitch to keep the stitches close together.

3 Use pink thread inside his nose – sew from side to side keeping the stitches close to fill up the space. This is called satin stitch.

4 Now sew Jacob's eyes with satin stitch. Go from side to side across the little oval shapes.

5 Rub off any chalk marks and you're done. Cute!

HOW TO STITCH...

Running stitch
Make a straight stitch then leave a space half the length in between before making another stitch.

Pass the needle in and out of the fabric to create a line of stitches and spaces.

OL!

TIP!

If you don't fancy sewing, use pink and black puffy fabric paints instead.

Meow!

WHY NOT?

Sew a matching book bag.

Back stitch

Make a stitch and a space, ~~like~~ the running stitch. Now take ~~t~~he needle back over the space ~~a~~nd bring it out again the same ~~d~~istance in front of your thread.

Keep repeating to make a solid line of stitches with no spaces.

Satin stitch

Make straight stitches from one edge of the shape you are filling to the other. Keep the stitches close together so you don't have any gaps.

Take care not to pull too tight and make the fabric bunch.

MAKE A SUPER HOMEWORK STATION!

Keep your stationery bits 'n' pieces oh-so-organised!

1 Put the shoebox lid aside for later. Measure across the bottom of the box and mark the middle point. Draw a line across the centre and up the sides.

Mark 6cm out from each side of the line and join the points to make a triangle like this. Do the same on the other side.

5 Cut the lid in half and slot in the pieces to make the fronts. Hold in place with some little bits of tape, then trim so the fronts are the same height as the sides.

7 Slot in some tubes and hold in place with double-sided tape. Ask an adult to make two holes through the centre panel and tie on a ribbon handle.

You'll need:

- ☑ Shoe box
- ☑ Cardboard tubes
- ☑ Old packaging like cereal boxes
- ☑ Double-sided sticky tape
- ☑ Scrap of ribbon

To decorate we used:

- ☑ Coloured Duck Tape from Asda
- ☑ Fabric tape from The Works

2 On the bottom, lightly score along the centre line with a pencil point. Now snip out the side triangles.

3 Stick some strips of double-sided tape across the bottom of the box and peel off the backing paper.

4 Now fold up along the centre line so the two halves stick together like this.

6 Get decorating! We used strips of bright tape, but you could paint the box or glue on pictures or paper scraps for a decoupage effect.

8

Use other packaging boxes to make more sections for little things.

Now fill it with all your stuff. Nice!

AAABB
CCDN&CS
EEFL|BG

53

NO SEW POP

Make it for your book nook!

You'll need:

- ⭐ 50cm of beige fleece
- ⭐ 25cm of pink fleece
- ⭐ Old pillow or cushions
- ⭐ Chalk
- ⭐ Fabric glue
- ⭐ Scraps of ribbon

The edges are braided together so you don't have to sew.

1 Fold your beige fleece in half and cut into two rectangles. Lay one on top of the other. Measure in 5cm from each edge and draw a chalk line — do this on all four sides. Snip out the four corner squares like this.

2 Now cut a fringe through both layers from the edges to your lines all the way round. Each fringe strip should be about 2cm wide — you don't have to be too neat.

5 Repeat by pushing the third strip up through the hole of the second strip. Keep going and a braided edge will start to appear. Braid round three sides and leave the last short side open.

6 Stuff your cushion with the filling from the old pillow or cushion — don't make it too fat or you'll lose the Pop Tart shape. Braid the last side closed, finish with a knot and tuck it in to hide.

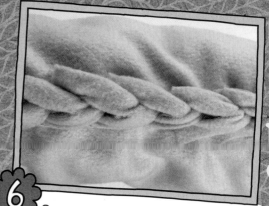

TART CUSHION

3 Fold each fringe strip in half and cut a little slit. This makes a little hole in each piece.

4 Lay out your fringed rectangle lengthwise. Start at the right-hand bottom corner and pick up the first fringe strip. Now pick up the strip to the left and push it up through the hole in the first one.

Gently pull it through so you can now see the hole of the second strip.

7 Cut your pink fleece in half. Now cut one piece into a wiggly icing splat like this. Glue it on to the cushion with the fabric glue.

8 Make sprinkles by cutting ribbon scraps into short pieces and glue these on top. Leave to dry and your Pop Tart is ready!

Jacqueline Wilson
ROSE RIVERS

READY, SE

Ruby's Tidy Tubs

1 Flatten out the jeans, measure up 30cm from the hem of one leg and cut it off. Turn the fabric inside out. Mark a straight line 2cm away from the cut edge.

2 Use a double thickness thread to stitch straight across the line. Use back stitch for extra strength.

3 Pinch and pin the corners like this and sew straight across here. Once that's done, turn the fabric to the right side.

4 Turn the top over two or three times to make a firm edge. Now squash down into a tub shape and fill with all your little bits and pieces.

WHY NOT? Decorate with some brooches or badges? Lovely!

56

T, MAKE!

You can make both these challenges from one pair of jeans.

Garnet's Vintage Journal

1 Cut a piece off a leg and cut it open close to the double stitched seam. Measure the cover of your notebook and cut the denim to fit. Use the seam edge to get a neat finish. Place the denim on the cover and put a mark at each spiral.

2 Now make a tiny snip at each mark. Glue the fabric to the front of your book — the snips let you push the fabric round the spirals like this.

3 Glue some ribbon or lace along the top and bottom edges.

Tie on a double strip of ribbon here.

Cut a strip from the waistband to fit the front — use the side with the button fastener attached — and glue it on.

Cut out a pocket and glue it to the front.

4 Fancy finishing touches!

Tie on ribbon and denim scraps too!

Tie a little book mark here.

Pop your pencils in the pocket!

Bring the ribbon round from the back and tie your journal closed.

Did you make something different?

MY NOTE

GARNET

57

Make Your Own Modelling Clay

It only takes 5 minutes!

You'll need: ★ 180g Corn flour   ★ 360g Bicarbonate of soda   ★ 280ml water

1 Put the corn flour and bicarbonate of soda into a saucepan. Mix with a little of the water to make a paste. Now gradually add the remaining water to get a milky liquid like this.

2 Ask an adult to help you heat the liquid on a medium heat, stirring all the time. Little bubbles will start to appear round the edges, but don't let the mix boil.

3 Keep stirring and after a few minutes the mix will start to thicken. When it's thick and doughy like this it's ready!

4 Tip the dough mix on to a surface lightly dusted with corn flour. Cover with a damp tea towel and leave to cool.

5 Knead the cool clay till smooth – it should be soft and easy to work with. Now you can start rolling, cutting and modelling!

TIP!
Keep the clay wrapped in cling film and only break off what you need. This will stop it from drying out.

To dry and harden the clay, leave it in a warm place for a couple of days or place in the oven at 50°C.

After 30 minutes in the oven, turn off the heat and leave for two hours. If the clay is still soft, bake again for another 30 minutes – don't let it brown or burn.

I made this little owl for my best friend, Owly!

1 Place a ball of clay between two pieces of cling film and roll out to around ½ cm thick. Use a round cookie cutter to cut a circle.

2 Use a pen lid to gently stamp on a feather pattern. Only stamp the feathers in the middle like this.

3 Carefully fold one side of the circle into the centre to make a wing. Now do the same to the other side.

4 Gently turn down the top of the circle to create two pointy owl ears. Use the pen lid to stamp on two round eyes.

5 Use a cocktail stick or pencil point to make two pupils in the centre of the eyes. Finish by sticking on a triangle beak made from a clay scrap.

You can decorate your dried clay with paint and glitter! How will you decorate your owl?

HETTY'S FEATHER BOOKMARKS!

The perfect reading accessory!

You'll need:
- ☑ Beads
- ☑ Wool (or string)
- ☑ Washi tape

1 Cut two lengths of washi tape roughly the same length and stick them down, overlapping them slightly.

Stick a piece of wool or string along the middle of the washi tape.

2 Cut two more lengths of washi tape and stick them down so it sandwiches the wool.

3 Snip the ends off to make a rectangle — be careful not to cut the string at the bottom!

4 Cut the washi tape into a feather shape, then snip diagonally into the middle to create a feather effect.

5 Tie a triple knot in the wool, then thread on two beads and tie another triple knot to keep them in place. Cut off any excess wool.

Recycle old things into a pretty room decoration.

CLOVER'S RAG WREATH!

You'll need:

☑ Old scrap paper
☑ Sticky tape
☑ Ribbon
☑ Scraps of fabric

1 Twist some old parcel paper or newspaper into a long sausage. Keep twisting, so the paper stays tight.

2 Bend the paper stick into a circle and tape the ends together like this.

3 Cut scraps of fabric into long strips — don't worry about being neat! Now tie the strips around the wreath in simple knots until all the paper is covered.

4 Fluff up the rags and trim off any extra-long bits. Tie a ribbon in a bow around the top with a loop at the end to hang it up. Lovely!

DIY Donut Squishy

You'll need:
- Odd socks
- Toy stuffing
- Felt square
- Fabric glue
- Sequins or beads

Eek! Do-nut squash me!

1 Turn your sock inside out and snip off the toe. Lay it flat and turn down about 3cm at the top. Pack the toy stuffing under the turned down edge all the way round.

2 When you have a nice, fat roll, pull the end of the sock to tighten. Now bring the end up over the roll, back down through the centre hole and pull tight again.

3 Repeat step 2 until you run out of sock. Pull and shape into a nice donut ring then glue down the edge with fabric glue. It should look like this...

4 Cut a felt icing splat to fit your donut, then fold in half to cut the little centre hole. Now glue it on to cover the sock edge. Add bead or sequin sprinkles to finish!

WHY NOT?
Use your squishy as a pin cushion. Swap the sequins for pins with brightly coloured ends - just push them into the filling.

62

ULTIMATE QUIZ MASTER

Show off your superior Jacqueline Wilson knowledge!

This is to certify that

..............Ava.................. has:

- ☐ Completed the This or That challenge
- ☐ Taken the Totally Tracy test
- ☐ Quizzed their way to the perfect JW read
- ☐ Found the perfect story to write
- ☐ Totally owned the Big JW Question Quiz
- ☐ Successfully solved the Who Am I? puzzles
- ☐ Played the Best Besties game

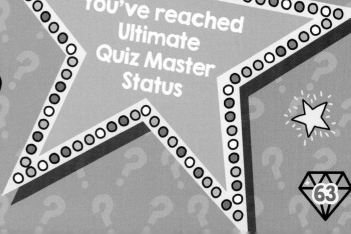

Congratulations!

You've reached Ultimate Quiz Master Status

63

Tracy's This Or That Test!

Which of my silly dares do you think Jacky and Nick would do?

Tick which one you'd choose!

Eat a strawberry dipped in mustard ☐ **OR** A pizza topped with Marmite ☐

Wear a unicorn horn in the supermarket ☐ **OR** Fairy wings to a posh restaurant ☐

Steal gold from a dragon ☐ **OR** Get past a giant spider ☐

Moo like a cow during a speech ☐ **OR** Cluck like a chicken ☐

what is the...

Bravest thing you've ever done?

Tell a teacher I thought they were being a dreadful bully.

Going down the black runs when I've been skiing — they're the steepest, most difficult slopes!

Most embarrassing thing you've ever done?

Jacky: Fall flat on my face at a posh dance.

Nick: At a very crowded party, I accidentally spilled an entire glass of red wine down the back of someone who was wearing a white jacket!

The naughtiest thing you've ever done?

Jacky: Climb over some very high railings to get out of a park at midnight!

Nick: I once managed to roll a huge tractor tyre into a large plate glass window when I was a boy.

All About You!

Write your own moments here!

Bravest:

Most embarrassing:

Naughtiest:

Tracy's Tremendous Trivia!

Answer the questions to find the words in the wordsearch!

ROUND 1 – THE STORY OF TRACY BEAKER

1. I grew up at The _ _ _ _ _ _ _ Ground.
2. Which of Justine's precious possessions did I supposedly break?
3. Who used to be my best friend?
4. What is Cam's surname?

ROUND 2 – I DARE YOU, TRACY BEAKER

5. What's my mum's name?
6. What did Roxanne dare me to tip over my head?
7. Who did I find hiding behind the curtain in the abandoned house?
8. One of my friends has a sporty nickname – what is it?

ROUND 3 – STARRING TRACY BEAKER

9. Which starring role did I have in the Christmas play?
10. What is my teacher called?
11. For Christmas, I bought lipstick, hand lotion, a copy of A Christmas Carol and a _ _ _ _ _ _ _ _ _ for my mum.
12. Which character starts a petition for me?

ROUND 4 – MY MUM TRACY BEAKER

13. Jess's full name is Jessica _ _ _ _ _ _ _ _ _ Camilla Beaker.
14. What martial arts class do I go to at the gym?
15. What kind of muffins does Cam bake and bring to Sean Godfrey's house?
16. Where do Jess and I live at the end of the story?

The Dumping Ground

66

Write your answers here and cross them out when you find them!

```
K J N B L U E B E L L S O W X A G A S Z
I I Y O L P Z O B L Q T Y G G K T W P Q
D R C V S B Z E Y L N P S J C O B A S
C U O K C W C T G P W A H M Y Z P W G N
E M M V B A A A E A C F B L L D D A H I
B Q O P L O V L L L C S K T A T W V E K
F W P K I N X E T V D V F O O Z J R T P
H V C D V N X I A L A R M C L O C K T M
L E P H H A G S N X B R Y K F H F X I I
N I K I N R C C Y G Y R R E B E U L B S
J M H D E O U R L A O G M K E S I U O L
J E E T O W V O R P G P H W A X S T Y O
Q R E K L X Z O A T G E J D R O N H Q Q
M P S V V R S G C G M I K U H S Z X Q B
C E N B B O D E X Z Q L I S V A L D N M
A W U B L H U H L Q Y U J Y C Z R F X F
```

1.
2.   /
3.
4.
5.
6.
7.
8.
9.
10.
11.
12.
13.
14.
15.
16.

ANSWERS: 1.Dumping 2.Alarm Clock 3.Lawson 4.Louise 5.Carly 6.Spaghetti 7.Alexander 8.Football 9.Scrooge 10.Simpkins 11.Necklace 12.Peter 13.Bluebell 14.Kick-boxing 15.Blueberry 16.Cooksea

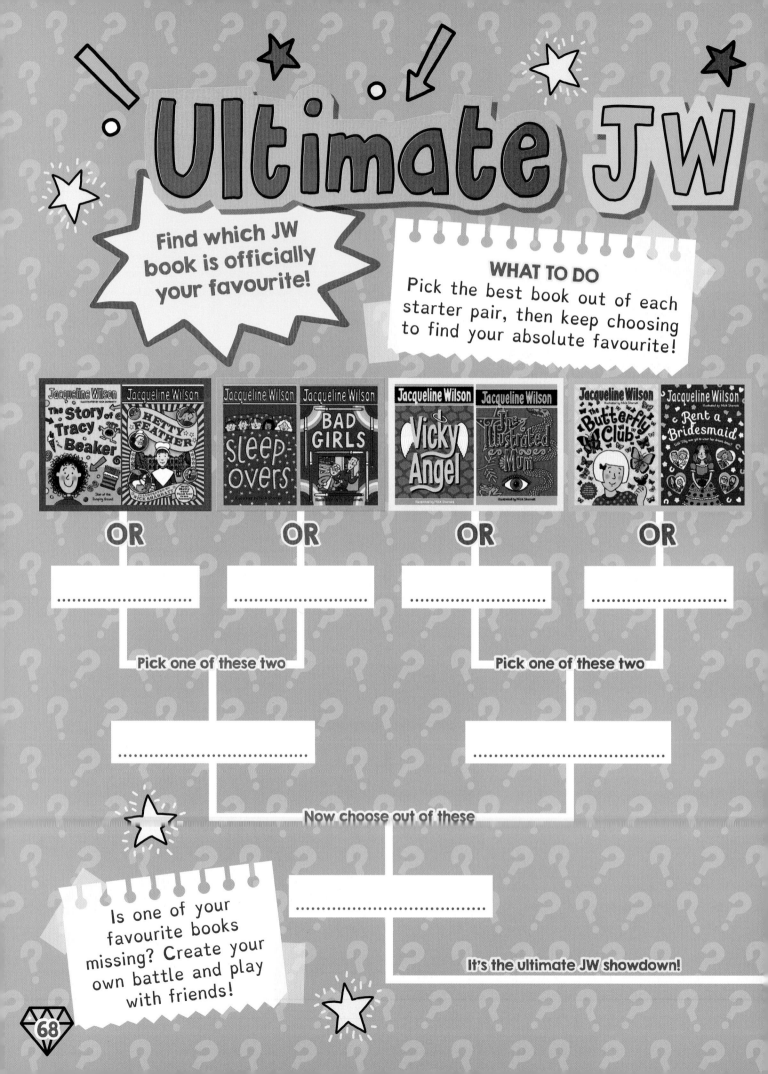

Ultimate JW

Find which JW book is officially your favourite!

WHAT TO DO
Pick the best book out of each starter pair, then keep choosing to find your absolute favourite!

OR   OR   OR   OR

Pick one of these two   Pick one of these two

Now choose out of these

Is one of your favourite books missing? Create your own battle and play with friends!

It's the ultimate JW showdown!

68

Book OFF!

OR   **OR**   **OR**   **OR**

....

Pick one of these two   Pick one of these two

....

Now choose out of these

....

Which will
you choose?

Celebrate by
re-reading it!

Your favourite JW Book is...

....

WHAT'S YOUR STORY STYLE?

Stuck for your next story? Get started here...

START

I cry at movies. — **YES** → Pretty in pink, that's me. — **YES** → I ♥ to daydream! — **YES**

I cry at movies. — **NO** → Puzzles are my favourite.

Pretty in pink, that's me. — **NO** → I have a BIG imagination.

I ♥ to daydream! — **NO** → History is my fave school subject!

Puzzles are my favourite. — **YES** → I have a BIG imagination. — **YES** → History is my fave school subject!

Puzzles are my favourite. — **NO** → Family is important!

I have a BIG imagination. — **NO** → I'm always up for an adventure!

History is my fave school subject! — **NO** → I hate not knowing stuff!

Family is important! — **YES** → I'm always up for an adventure! — **YES** → I hate not knowing stuff!

Family is important! — **NO** → Surprises are the best!

I'm always up for an adventure! — **NO** → Reality is boring!

Surprises are the best! — **YES** → Reality is boring!

Reality is boring! — **NO** → I wish I could time travel. — **YES** → I hate not knowing stuff!

Reality is boring! → **YES** → Unicorns are sooo pretty!

Surprises are the best! — **NO** → I wish I could time travel.

I wish I could time travel. — **NO** → Unicorns are sooo pretty!

Unicorns are sooo pretty! — **NO**

NO

SWEET ROMANCE!

You've got a date with romance!

READ

Jacqueline Wilson
GIRLS ♥ IN ♥ LOVE

WRITE

- Cookie and Biscuits meet at a baking contest
- Hetty and Bertie bump into each other at a dance hall
- Tracy and Peter take a midnight stroll on a beach

Magic is real.

YES

NO

FUN FAIRYTALE!

Imagine a world full of fantasy and magic!

READ

Jacqueline Wilson
FOUR CHILDREN and IT

Can your wildest wishes really come true?

WRITE

- A mermaid who saves someone from drowning
- Normal girl by day... unicorn by night
- A school for vampires, werewolves and ogres

YES

I like sad endings.

YES

YES

YES

HISTORY MYSTERY!

A period plot filled with adventure!

READ

Jacqueline Wilson
HETTY FEATHER

WRITE

- A Victorian nanny who solves a kidnapping
- A WW2 evacuee who finds buried treasure
- A girl in the 1950s who saves the life of Queen Elizabeth II

YES

My fave books are set in the past.

NO

NO

FAMILY DRAMA!

Nothing is more exciting than real life!

READ

Jacqueline Wilson
MY MUM TRACY BEAKER

WRITE

- An only child who discovers a secret sibling
- A huge family reunion, ending with a big fight
- Twins having a prank war that goes horribly wrong

Jacky's Killer Quiz!

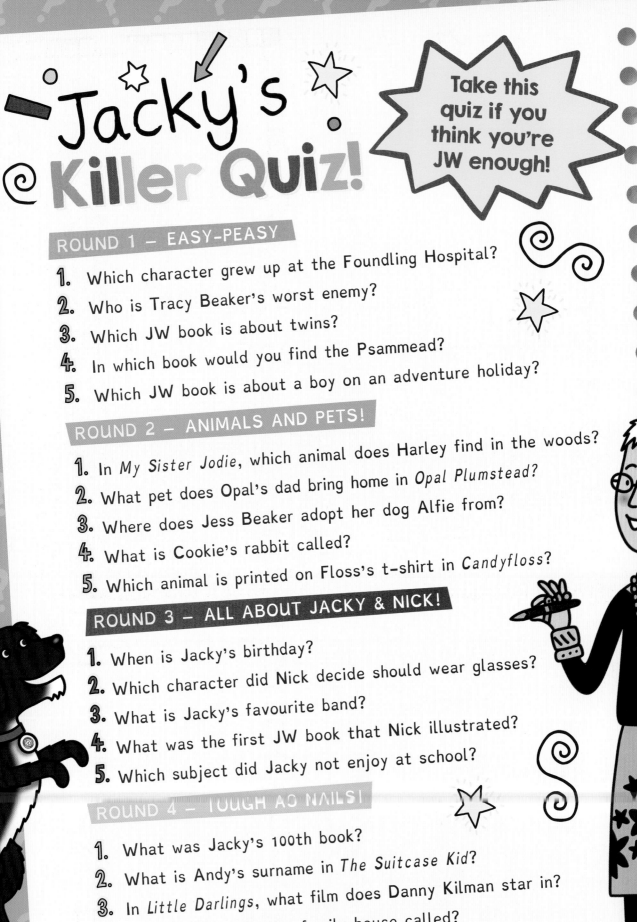

Take this quiz if you think you're JW enough!

ROUND 1 – EASY-PEASY

1. Which character grew up at the Foundling Hospital?
2. Who is Tracy Beaker's worst enemy?
3. Which JW book is about twins?
4. In which book would you find the Psammead?
5. Which JW book is about a boy on an adventure holiday?

ROUND 2 – ANIMALS AND PETS!

1. In *My Sister Jodie*, which animal does Harley find in the woods?
2. What pet does Opal's dad bring home in *Opal Plumstead*?
3. Where does Jess Beaker adopt her dog Alfie from?
4. What is Cookie's rabbit called?
5. Which animal is printed on Floss's t-shirt in *Candyfloss*?

ROUND 3 – ALL ABOUT JACKY & NICK!

1. When is Jacky's birthday?
2. Which character did Nick decide should wear glasses?
3. What is Jacky's favourite band?
4. What was the first JW book that Nick illustrated?
5. Which subject did Jacky not enjoy at school?

ROUND 4 – TOUGH AS NAILS!

1. What was Jacky's 100th book?
2. What is Andy's surname in *The Suitcase Kid*?
3. In *Little Darlings*, what film does Danny Kilman star in?
4. What is Rose Rivers' family house called?
5. In *The Butterfly Club*, which triplet has a scar on her chin?

72

ROUND 1

1. ....
2. ....
3. ....
4. ....
5. ....

ROUND 2

1. ....
2. ....
3. ....
4. ....
5. ....

ROUND 3

1. ....
2. ....
3. ....
4. ....
5. ....

ROUND 4

1. ....
2. ....
3. ....
4. ....
5. ....

WRITE YOUR SCORE HERE!

_____ /20

0 - 7
New Recruit!

Maybe you haven't quite got around to reading all of Jacky's books yet, but that's OK — it just means you have lots of amazing books ahead of you!

8 - 14
Star Student!

Amazing effort! There are some JW books you haven't read yet, but you're well on your way to discovering them all and becoming a JW expert!

15 - 20
Certified Expert!

Take a bow — you know everything there is to know about JW! We bet you've read almost all the JW books and collect *The Official JW Mag* too!

ANSWERS
Round 4 – 1. Opal Plumstead, 2. West, 3. Milky Star, 4. Lion House, 5. Maddie
Round 3 – 1. 17 December, 2. Jess Beaker, 3. Queen, 4. The Story of Tracy Beaker, 5. Maths.
Round 2 – 1. Badgers, 2. A budgie, 3. Battersea Dogs and Cats Home, 4. Birthday, 5. Koala.
Round 1 – 1. Hetty Feather, 2. Justine Littlewood, 3. Double Act, 4. Four Children and It, 5. Cliffhanger.

73

WHO AM I?

Use the clues to discover who's who!

Riddle-Reveal!

Solve the riddle to reveal the JW character's name!

My first is in sleet but not in fleet
My second is the third in an hour
My third is in a barn but not in bar
My fourth is the first in sour
My fifth is in need as well as in week
And my sixth is the start of tower

. . . .

Pet Prompt!

Match the characters to the animals in their stories!

Jess

Lucky

Floss

Mabel

Verity

Alfie

Description Detective!

Use the clues to cross out characters until you're left with one!

Clue #1 I'm from the past
Clue #2 My name is a precious stone
Clue #3 I'm a circus performer

Garnet   Shirley   Hetty   Diamond   Opal   Pearl

74

The BFF Test!

Put your friendship to the test!

WHAT TO DO

Cut out the questionnaire and fill in the answers about your bestie. Then ask them to answer about you. No peeking! Swap to do the marking. Get one point for every correct answer!

ABOUT YOUR BESTIE!

POINTS

Middle name: ....

Star sign: ....

Eye colour: ....

Dream job: ....

BFF'S FAVE THINGS!

Book: ....

Movie: ....

TV Show: ....

Animal: ....

Colour: ....

MY PAL PREFERS...

Drawing OR Writing ....

High heels OR Trainers ....

YouTube OR PopJam ....

Unicorn OR Mermaid ....

Cake OR Ice cream ....

TOTAL SCORE _____

75

Check your score!

0 - 5
Sounds like your friendship is pretty new – time to get to know each other better! How about a sleepover or BFF day out?

6 - 11
Yay! Your friendship is super-strong and you know lots about each other – but there's always new stuff to learn! Time for a game of truth or dare...

12 - 14
Wow, you know your bestie as well as you know yourself – are you two twins, by any chance? It's like you share a mind!

ABOUT YOUR BESTIE!

POINTS

Middle name: ....

Star sign: ....

Eye colour: ....

Dream job: ....

BFF'S FAVE THINGS!

Book: ....

Movie: ....

TV Show: ....

Animal: ....

Colour: ....

MY PAL PREFERS...

Drawing **OR** Writing ....

High heels **OR** Trainers ....

YouTube **OR** PopJam ....

Unicorn **OR** Mermaid ....

Cake **OR** Ice cream ....

TOTAL SCORE _____

MY STORY

IDEAS! IDEAS! IDEAS!

Start your story-writing adventure by coming up with some brilliant ideas. Pick your favourite to turn into a book!

Be Inspired!

Ideas can come from almost anywhere...

- A strange dream you've had
- Something you overheard at the shops
- A lesson at school
- A song you've heard
- Flicking through old JW Mags
- A story you've read
- Something you saw on a walk
- Memories

Genre Generator!

Not sure what kind of story to write? Let fate decide!

What to do:

- Place a pencil in the middle and spin it.
- 1st spin — note down which genre you land on in the inner section.
- 2nd spin — find your next genre from the outer section.
- Mash your two genres together and get writing!

I'm going to write a space romance!

Comedy · Mystery · Fairy-tale · Spooky · Superhero · Space · Historical · Adventure · Family · War · Pirate · Animal · Spy · Western · Friendship · Romance

SCHEDULE!

week 2-3

WHAT IF...

Daydream away!

The best part of writing is making up the story in your mind!

Now that you've got your basic idea, start daydreaming all the different directions your story could take.

Scribble down notes in your journal to keep track. Just ask yourself this question: What if this happened...?

....

....

....

....

....

....

....

....

....

My JOURNAL

CREATE A CHARACTER

week 4-5

Who will star in your story? You'll need at least one main character, some side characters and an opponent!

Jot down some character ideas here — turn to page 10 for inspiration!

My main character is: ....

Their best friend is: ....

Their family are: ....

Their biggest enemy is: ....

week 6
STORY SYNOPSIS!

Have you ever read the write-up on the back of a book? It's a few sentences that give you an idea what the story will be about.

Here's an example:

When Floss's mum and her husband move to Australia, will Floss go with them or stay with her dad?

Dad's not much good at tidying up, but together they have fun, eating chip butties and candyfloss from the local fair. When disaster strikes, they find themselves homeless. Can their fairground friends help out?

AUSTRALIA SYDNEY

Can you tell which of my books this synopsis is about?

Now sum up what will happen in your own story!

....

....

....

week 7-9
PLAN YOUR PLOT!

Use this handy diagram to record the main parts of your story!

Marvellous Middle!

3. The Climax
Write what happens when the problem or conflict reaches a high point — it's the most exciting part of the story!

Brilliant Beginning!

2. Rising Action
Build up to the story's main problem or conflict.

4. Falling Action
How does the problem or conflict get solved?

Fabulous Finish!

1. Background Info
The start of the story is where characters and setting are introduced. Try to begin with something that really grabs your reader's attention!

5. Resolution
Write how things end up here. Will it be a sad ending or a happy one — or even a cliffhanger!

CHARACTER CONUNDRUM!

Time to get to know your main character better! Put yourself in their mind and answer these questions for them.

My full name is:

Nickname:

Birthday:

Star Sign:

My hair is:

My eyes are:

I like to wear:

My favourite ice cream flavour is:

My favourite animal is:

How I met my best friend:

At school, I'm brilliant at:

A+ REPORT CARD

But I'm terrible at:

My biggest worry is:

My most embarrassing moment is:

My dream job is:

Use this template to answer questions for all of your characters!

I get scared when:

week 15-16

SORT YOUR SETTING!

Your setting is important. Imagine a story taking place in blank space — so boring!

A location can create different effects. Add tension with an old, spooky house or inspire wonder with a fantasy world.

Time Warp!

Remember, it's not just about *where* it is, but *when* it is! When will your story happen? Decide here!

PAST ☐ PRESENT ☐ FUTURE ☐

If your story is set in the past, read non-fiction about the era. You can also read fiction set during the time to get a feel of what life was like.

Think about how the world will have changed if you're setting your story in the future. What new technology will there be?

Map It Out!

Use scrap paper to draw a map of your world. This will be useful when you're writing because you can quickly reference your map for help as your characters are moving around.

Dazzling Description!

Make your world come to life with detail. Choose a key place on your map and fill the circles below with words to describe how it looks, sounds and smells.

LOOKS

SOUNDS

SMELLS

Week 17-19

WHAT'S THE PLAN?

Now it's time to get things in order! Plan an outline by writing down what will happen in each chapter. Turn to **page 88-89** for more help on this.

Week 20-25

READY, SET, WRITE!

There's nothing else to do but sit down and start writing. Let your words flow and don't worry about making mistakes — you'll get to perfect it later!

Week 26-28

READ IT!

Read your draft and note down changes you could make, but don't fix anything yet. Look out for common themes like bullying, friendship or love. This will help you later!

Week 29-34

BE BRUTAL!

This is when you need to be tough and cut things that don't work like pointless scenes and characters, but you can also add scenes and dialogue too to expand on your themes.

Week 35-46

RINSE & REPEAT!

Put your book away for a week, then read it through and make notes just like you did with your first draft. Then begin re-writing again to transform your second draft into a fantastic final edit.

Week 47-52

FINISH LINE!

Correct spelling mistakes, weird grammar and poor punctuation, then ask somebody to check it again! Well done — you've finished your masterpiece! Now it's time to start practising your author's autograph!

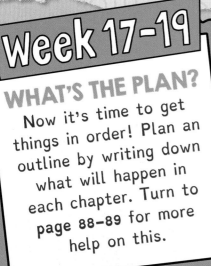

Creating Story Char[acters]

Mind maps are a great way to keep track of your characters.

Writing down profiles for each character will help you keep all the little details right.

You can add more information whenever you need to — your character's friends and family, personality traits, likes and dislikes.

The more you look at your maps, the more you will remember. Eventually you'll be able to picture all your character details in your head.

JOHN & PEG COTTON

JEM
ELIZA
ROSIE
NORA
BESS
MARCUS
NAT

MARTHA
SAUL
GIDEON

TANGLEFIELD'S

TAN[

MADAME
ADELINE

FOUNDLING SIBLINGS

SIBLINGS

FATHER & MOTHER

FOSTER FAMILY

THE FOUNDLING HOSPITAL

Jacqueline Wilson
HETTY FEATHER

FOUNDLING NO. 25629

TEACHERS

MISS NEWMAN
MISS MORLEY

FRIENDS

NURSE WINTERS[
HARRIET
POLLY
SISSY & LIL
MISS SMITH
IDA

ENEMIES

SHEILA
MATRON PIGFACE
MATRON STINKING BOTTOMLY

IDA

Look at this map for Hetty then try making some of your own...

MR BUCHANAN (WRITER)

MRS BRISKETT (HOUSEKEEPER)
SARAH (PARLOURMAID)

THE MYSTERIOUS
MADAME BERENICE

EMPLOYED AS MAID
OF ALL WORK

SWEETHEART

BERTIE THE
BUTCHER'S BOY

Jacqueline Wilson
SAPPHIRE
BATTERSEA

BIGNOR

MAMA

MR CLARENDON'S
CURIOSITIES

FRIENDS

THE GREENWOOD FAMILY

FANTASTIC FREDA THE
FEMALE GIANT

EMERALD, THE AMAZING
POCKET–SIZED MERMAID

PAPA & MAMA
CHARLOTTE
MAISIE
BABY FLORA

THE WORLD OF
HETTY FEATHER

A complete guide
to Hetty's life!

Jacqueline Wilson
EMERALD
STAR

CARTERS BRAY

MONKSBY

FRIEND

LIZZIE

BOBBIE WATERS &
WIFE, KATHERINE

FRIEND

JANET

TANGLEFIELD'S
CIRCUS

CHILDREN

MINA
EZRA

MADAME ADELINE
THE SILVER TUMBLERS
DIAMOND

STICKY NOTES STORY MAP!

Use this hack to keep track of your story!

You'll need: ☑ **A3 paper or card** ☑ **Sticky notes**

STEP ONE: MAKE YOUR MAP

1 Read the first chapter of your story.

2 Write down the chapter number at the top of a sticky note, then try to summarise what happens in one sentence underneath.

3 Stick the note in the top left corner of your A3 card.

4 Now do the same for every chapter of your story, placing them next to each other in order, like this!

1. Destiny's mum plans to reunite with Danny Kilman at a premiere.

2. Sunset notices Destiny and her mum at the premiere.

3. Destiny's mum decides to find Danny Kilman's house.

4. Sunset lets Destiny in and discovers that Destiny is her sister.

5. Destiny signs up for the school talent competition.

6. Sunset sends a jacket to Destiny and overhears her dad cheating.

7. Destiny impresses at rehearsal and writes back to Sunset.

8. A bad article is published about Danny.

9. Destiny only comes second to last in the competition.

10. Danny invites his girlfriend to Sweetie's party, causing a fight.

11. Destiny wins the evening talent competition.

12. Sunset suggests Destiny should star on their TV show.

13. Destiny and Danny are finally reunited.

TOP TIP!

If your chapters are narrated by different characters, like Destiny and Sunset in *Little Darlings*, use different coloured sticky notes for each of them.

STEP TWO: Q&A

Now you can see an overview of your entire book, take a look at each chapter and ask yourself these questions about each:

1 What does this chapter do? Does it introduce a character or move the story along?

2 Is this chapter important to the story or can it be cut?

3 Does this chapter follow on from the last chapter or does it need a new chapter in between to help it make sense?

4 What would happen if you moved this chapter to the end or beginning?

EXAMPLE!

3. Destiny's mum decides to find Danny Kilman's house.

This chapter is important because it moves the story along. Do not cut!

It works with the chapter before it.

Moving this chapter to the beginning might add tension — the reader wouldn't know that Destiny is Danny's daughter!

STEP THREE: EXPERIMENT

There are no rules to say you have to start at the beginning and finish at the end!

1 Take away the chapters you don't need and add in any extras you need to write.

2 Have fun re-ordering your sticky notes to see what effect it has on the story! Remember, you can always move them back later.

3 Keep shuffling things around until you're happy with it.

What if Jacky had started *Little Darlings* with the last chapter when Danny and Destiny finally reunite? We moved chapter 13 to chapter 1 and came up with an alternate ending!

1.
~~13.~~ Destiny and Danny are finally reunited.

13. Destiny and Danny sing Sunset's song on the TV show.

STEP FOUR: EDIT SPREE!

Now you've decided on your new structure, it's time to go through your first draft and start editing! Turn to page 85 for tips.

Create a Cover!

How to design a best-selling book cover!

Now you have your book all planned out, it's time to design a cover! Make one that will stand out on the shelves and encourage readers to buy it.

BE INSPIRED!
Take a look at the books on your shelves. What made them stand out to you? Write a list here:

PUBLISHER'S BRIEF!
The publisher of your book has asked you to include these important elements. Tick them off when they've been added:

- [ ] Include one or two main characters
- [ ] Your title should be bold and stand out
- [ ] Make it bright and colourful to appeal to your fans
- [ ] Include your name so readers know who the author is!

NICK'S ADVICE!
Nick begins by sketching different ideas called rough drawings, then he picks his favourite and works on it until he's happy!

Here are a couple of my rough drawings for *My Sister Jodie* and the final version. What makes the final cover better?

JACQUELINE WILSON
MY SISTER JODIE

JACQUELINE WILSON
My Sister Jodie

Jacqueline Wilson
MY SISTER JODIE!

WORTH 1000 WORDS!

Your cover should give readers a glimpse into the story and make them want to find out more!

Use the templates for your rough drawings!

BACK COVER!

Write some enticing text for the back cover. It should be just enough to get readers interested without revealing any spoilers!

FRIENDLY FEEDBACK!

Show your rough drawings to friends and family. Ask which one stands out to them the most and why.

See you on the bookshelves soon!

JACKY ASKS, NICK ANSWERS!

Fill in your answers too!

Time for Nick to reveal all!

What would you like to be if you weren't an illustrator?

I'd like to be a set designer for films and television!

Movie Script

My dream job is:

....

....

....

Who is your favourite artist?

LS Lowry. Lowry's work inspired me to have a go at creating of my own crowd scenes. I did this market scene when I was nine and it was put up in my school hall!

DID YOU KNOW?

LS Lowry was a popular painter born in 1887. He liked to paint crowds of people — sometimes hundreds in one scene!

If you were forced to take up a particular sport, which would you choose?

Tennis.